# Close Encounters

## People Jesus helped from the New Testament

Pete and Anne Woodcock

Jesus and You: Close Encounters
© Pete and Anne Woodcock/The Good Book Company 2012

Published by
The Good Book Company Ltd
1 Blenheim Road
Epsom, Surrey KT19 9AP, UK
Tel (UK): 0333 123 0880
Tel (Int): (+44) 208 942 0880
email: admin@thegoodbook.co.uk

Websites
**UK:** www.thegoodbook.co.uk
**N America:** www.thegoodbook.com
**Australia:** www.thegoodbook.com.au
**New Zealand:** www.thegoodbook.co.nz

ISBN: 9781908317704
Printed in China
Design by André Parker

Cover image features a celestial eye goldfish

# Contents

This handbook is designed to be used with the **Jesus and You: Close Encounters DVD** also available from The Good Book Company. (DVD ISBN: 9781908317711)

A free downloadable **Leader's Guide** is available on our website: **www.thegoodbook.co.uk/closeencounters**

# Welcome to Close Encounters

We hope that you will enjoy these four sessions. They will introduce you to Jesus Christ and his teaching.

In this booklet you will find a number of things to help you:

- Questions that you can talk about in your group

- Space to write down what you learn, if you want to

- The parts of the Bible that we will look at

- A summary of each DVD talk that we will watch

- Space to write down your own questions, comments or problems

Close Encounters is for anyone and everyone who wants to find out about Jesus Christ. This means that...

- some of you know something about these stories of Jesus—but some of you don't know anything.

- some of you have been to church—but some of you are completely new to the Christian faith.

- some of you enjoy reading, writing and studying—but some of you haven't done this for years, and perhaps you never enjoyed it even then.

- some of you may be learning to speak English.

Whoever you are, don't worry—your group leader will help you and will explain everything you need to know.

So, time to get started and get into Close Encounters...

# 1 The man who came through the roof
## Luke 5 v 17-26

### Think about people's needs...

■ What do people think is their biggest need today?

### The story

■ Listen to the story Jesus told: Luke 5 v 17-26.
■ You can read it for yourself on p12.

**Optional Extra**

**Test yourself:** how much can you remember?
Answer the questions (in pairs, if you prefer).

■ Why did people want to see Jesus?

■ How do we know that there were lots of people listening to Jesus?

■ How did the paralysed man get around in this story?

■ How did his friends get him into the house?

■ What did Jesus do first for the paralysed man?

■ Who else saw and heard what Jesus did?

■ What did these people think of Jesus?

■ They believed that only one person could forgive sins. Who?

■ How did Jesus show that he had authority on earth to forgive sins?

# Desperate need

**Listen to the first part of the story again:**
**Luke 5 v 17-20**
You can read it for yourself on p12.

## Think about it

1.  Everyone knows that Jesus was a great miracle-worker and a prophet (someone who brings a message from God).

    Imagine Jesus is living up the road. What do you think most people would ask him to do for them?

2.  These friends go to a lot of effort to get help for their friend. Look at verse 20. What is surprising, and a bit disappointing? (Clue: Think about what Jesus does AND what he doesn't do.)

3.  What does Jesus think this man's biggest need is?

 **DOWNLOAD 1:1**

(Summary on p42)

4.  When people hear the word "sin", what do they usually think?

**5.** What do you think the word "sin" means?

Look at the descriptions of "sin" below.
Are they good or bad descriptions of sin?

**a** sin = doing something very bad (like child abuse or murder)

**b** sin = sex

**c** sin = doing what you want

**d** sin = not loving God and his ways

**6.** Jesus shows us that the most important thing he can do for us is to forgive our sins. Why is that the most important thing?

**Ask yourself:**

- Do I know that I am a sinner—a helpless, hopeless outcast from God?
- Do I see that my biggest need is to have my sin forgiven?
- Do I understand that only Jesus can help me?

# Shocking words

**Listen to the next part of the story: Luke 5 v 20-21**
You can read it for yourself on p12.

## Think about it

1. Here are some things that people often say about forgiveness:

   **a** "I made a mistake when I lied. I let myself down. I need to forgive myself and move on."

   **b** "She'll never forgive me for what I did."

   **c** "I feel terrible. I can't forgive myself."

   **d** "He's forgiven me, so everything's OK now."

Look at what the Pharisees and teachers of the law say in verse 21. What do they believe about forgiveness?

How is that different from the sentences you have just read?

**DOWNLOAD 1:2**

(Summary on p42)

2. What sort of evidence shows us that Jesus is God (the one who can forgive sins)?

# Sure proof

**Listen to the last part of the story: Luke 5 v 22-26**
You can read it for yourself on p12.

### Think about it

**1.** How did Jesus show that he is the one who can forgive sins?

▪ What did everyone think (see v 26)?

**2.** Remember that this man was a helpless, hopeless outcast.
How was his whole life immediately changed by Jesus?

**DOWNLOAD 1:3**

(Summary on p42)

## The big questions

Jesus is the sin-forgiver. The friends of the paralysed man didn't let the crowd or the roof get in the way of coming to Jesus. They believed that only he could help. And they found out that he could do far more than they ever imagined.

■ Do you believe in Jesus?
■ What is stopping you from coming to Jesus?

"All the prophets give witness about [Jesus]. They say that all who believe in him have their sins forgiven through his name."

Acts 10 v 43 (The Bible: New International Reader's Version)

**My questions and comments**

# 1 Bible text

## The man who came through the roof Luke 5 v 17-26

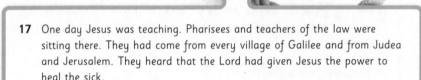

**17** One day Jesus was teaching. Pharisees and teachers of the law were sitting there. They had come from every village of Galilee and from Judea and Jerusalem. They heard that the Lord had given Jesus the power to heal the sick.

**18** Some men came carrying a man who could not walk. He was lying on a mat. They tried to take him into the house to place him in front of Jesus.

**19** They could not find a way to do this because of the crowd. So they went up on the roof. Then they lowered the man on his mat through the opening in the roof tiles. They lowered him into the middle of the crowd, right in front of Jesus.

**20** When Jesus saw that they had faith, he said, "Friend, your sins are forgiven."

**21** The Pharisees and the teachers of the law began to think, "Who is this fellow who says such an evil thing? Who can forgive sins but God alone?"

**22** Jesus knew what they were thinking. So he asked, "Why are you thinking these things in your hearts?

**23** "Is it easier to say, 'Your sins are forgiven'? Or to say, 'Get up and walk'?

**24** "I want you to know that the Son of Man has authority on earth to forgive sins." So he spoke to the man who could not walk. "I tell you," he said, "get up. Take your mat and go home."

**25** Right away, the man stood up in front of them. He took his mat and went home praising God.

**26** Everyone was amazed and gave praise to God. They were filled with wonder. They said, "We have seen unusual things today."

# 2 The man silenced by a demon
## Luke 11 v 14-26

**Summary so far:**

▢ Jesus is the sin-forgiver because Jesus is God. Only he can help people like us, who are helpless, hopeless outcasts from God.

## Think about amazing claims...

■ Let's say someone in this room claims things like...
  ▢ they can get you right with God.
  ▢ they are the judge of the whole universe.
  ▢ they are the king of everyone everywhere.
  ▢ they can make a perfect, new universe!

■ Could they be...
  **a** mad?
  **b** evil / controlled by something evil?
  **c** telling the truth?

■ What would you expect to see if they were...
  **a** mad?
  **b** evil /controlled by something evil?
  **c** telling the truth?

■ Which explanation best fits someone like Hitler?

Optional Extra

**The story**

■ Listen to this true story about Jesus: Luke 11 v 14-26
■ You can read it for yourself on p20-21.

**Test yourself:** how much can you remember?
Answer the true or false questions (in pairs, if you prefer).

■ Jesus used the power of Beelzebub (the prince of demons) to drive out demons. **T / F**

■ Jesus knew what the people around him were thinking. **T / F**

■ Jesus said that a kingdom that fights against itself will be destroyed. **T / F**

■ Jesus said that when a strong man is armed and guards his house, no one can attack him. **T / F**

■ Jesus said that someone stronger can take away the strong man's things. **T / F**

■ Jesus said that an evil spirit doesn't like to live in clean, tidy house. **T / F**

# Good or evil?

**Listen to the first part of the story again: Luke 11 v 14-22**
You can read it yourself on p20.

**Think about it**

1. What were some people accusing Jesus of?

**2.** It's shocking to say that Jesus uses the power of evil.

Let's look at why these people came to such a strong opinion about Jesus. (These questions will help you answer this.)

■ What had they just seen Jesus do?

■ What did this miracle show them about Jesus?

■ They wanted to show that Jesus was bad, so that they would have a reason to ignore him. There was only one way they could do this. What was it?

■ Look at the opinion they came to about Jesus. Was it sensible?

**3.** There's a different response to Jesus in verse 16. Why is this response ridiculous? (Think about what they have just seen.)

■ Why do you think they ask for this?

16

DOWNLOAD 2:1

(Summary on p43)

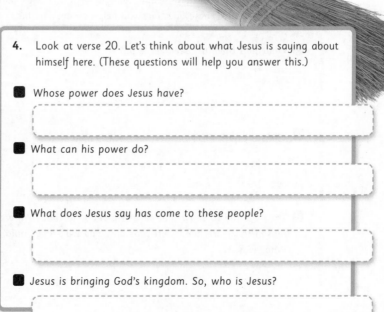

4. Look at verse 20. Let's think about what Jesus is saying about himself here. (These questions will help you answer this.)

■ Whose power does Jesus have?

■ What can his power do?

■ What does Jesus say has come to these people?

■ Jesus is bringing God's kingdom. So, who is Jesus?

**Ask yourself:**

■ Have I realised that there is an evil power in this world who is trying to ruin and destroy everything God has made?

■ Where do I think Jesus' power comes from?

# Strong v stronger

**Think about it**

1. In verses 21 and 22 Jesus explains his miracle, which we read about in verse 14.

Look at verse 14 and write the missing information in the chart.

| | Jesus' story (v 21-23) | Jesus and the demon (v 14) |
|---|---|---|
| Who is the winner? | The stronger man | |
| Who is the loser? | The strong man | |
| What does the loser lose? | His possessions ("what he owns", v 21) | |
| What does the winner take control of? | The strong man's possessions (v 22) | |

**DOWNLOAD 2:2**

(Summary on p43)

**Ask yourself:**

◼ How might Satan be trying to keep me out of God's kingdom?

# Clean up or get rescued?

**Listen to the last part of what Jesus says: Luke 11 v 23-26**
You can read it yourself on p20-21.

## Think about it

**1.** What happened to the evil spirit in verse 14 (the strong man in the first story—verses 21-22)?

**2.** Now compare the second story told by Jesus, in verses 24-26.

■ What can the evil spirit do in the second story (verse 24)?

■ Jesus pictures a person as a house. What can't this person do?

■ What does this person need?

■ Who is missing from the second story? (Compare verse 22.)

**DOWNLOAD 2:3**

(Summary on p43)

## The big questions

Jesus claims to be the stronger man that you need to rescue you from the power of Satan.

- Is Jesus mad, evil or telling the truth?
- How are you fighting against the power of evil that is trying to control your life? Are you trying to clean up your life by yourself, or do you need a rescuer?

"[Jesus] took away the weapons of the powers and authorities (Satan and his demons). He made a public show of them. He won the battle over them by dying on the cross."

Colossians 2 v 15 (The Bible: New International Reader's Version)

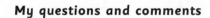

**My questions and comments**

# 2   Bible text

## The man silenced by a demon
### Luke 11 v 14-26

**14**   Jesus was driving out a demon. The man who had the demon could not speak. When the demon left, the man began to speak. The crowd was amazed.

**15**   But some of them said, "Jesus is driving out demons by the power of Beelzebub, the prince of demons."

**16**   Others put Jesus to the test by asking for a miraculous sign from heaven.

**17**   Jesus knew what they were thinking. So he said to them, "Any kingdom that fights against itself will be destroyed. A family that is divided against itself will fall.

**18**   "If Satan fights against himself, how can his kingdom stand? I say this because of what you claim. You say I drive out demons by the power of Beelzebub.

**19**   "Suppose I do drive out demons with Beelzebub's help. With whose help do your followers drive them out? So then, they will be your judges.

**20**   "But suppose I drive out demons with the help of God's powerful finger. Then God's kingdom has come to you.

**21**   "When a strong man is completely armed and guards his house, what he owns is safe.

**22**   "But when someone stronger attacks, he is overpowered. The attacker takes away the armour the man had trusted in. Then he divides up what he has stolen.

**23**   "Anyone who is not with me is against me. Anyone who does not gather sheep with me scatters them.

**24** "What happens when an evil spirit comes out of a man? It goes through dry areas looking for a place to rest. But it doesn't find it. Then it says, 'I will return to the house I left.'

**25** "When it arrives there, it finds the house swept clean and put in order.

**26** "Then the evil spirit goes and takes seven other spirits more evil than itself. They go in and live there. That man is worse off than before."

# 3 The sick woman and the dying girl
## Mark 5 v 21-43

**Summary so far:**

- Jesus is the sin-forgiver because Jesus is God. Only Jesus can help people like us, who are helpless, hopeless outcasts from God.
- Jesus is the "stronger man". Only he can rescue us from the power of Satan.

## Think about peoples' dreams...

- Here are some things that people hope for in life. How does death ruin and destroy each of these hopes?

  - A happy life
  - Good health
  - Success for their children
  - Plenty of money
  - Early retirement
  - Doing something that people will remember them for

- Death is the enemy of all our hopes. How do people try to comfort themselves when death comes?

- In history there have been lots of clever thinkers, powerful rulers, politicians, inventors and scientists. There have been many different ideas and religions. But has anyone ever found a cure for death?

**The story**

- Listen to this true story about Jesus: Mark 5 v 21-43
- You can read it for yourself on p31-32.

**Optional Extra**

**Test yourself:** how much can you remember?
Answer the questions (in pairs, if you prefer).

A  At the beginning of the story...

    **a** Jesus decided he would heal Jairus' daughter later.

    **b** Jesus immediately went with Jairus to heal his daughter.

    **c** Jesus didn't want to heal Jairus' daughter.

B  **a** The sick woman stopped Jesus and asked him to heal her.

    **b** The sick woman wanted to be healed and to talk with Jesus.

    **c** The sick woman didn't want to meet Jesus but wanted to be healed.

C  **a** For 12 years the woman's sickness had got worse.

    **b** For 12 years lots of doctors had helped the woman.

    **c** For 12 years the woman hadn't bothered about her sickness.

D  **a** The woman was healed when Jesus touched her.

    **b** The woman was healed when Jesus spoke to her.

    **c** The woman was healed when she touched Jesus' clothes.

E  **a** Jesus said that his power had healed the woman.

    **b** Jesus said that the woman's faith had healed her.

    **c** Jesus didn't know what had healed the woman.

F  Jesus said Jairus' daughter was only sleeping because...

    **a** it was so easy for him to bring her back to life.

    **b** everyone had made a mistake.

    **c** he didn't want to upset her parents.

# "Don't bother Jesus"

**Listen to the first part of the story again: Mark 5 v 21-34**
You can read it yourself on p31-32.

### Think about it

1. This women's situation was hopeless.
   How does the story show that?

2. Imagine what this woman was thinking as she came near to Jesus.
   Which thought best fits her story?

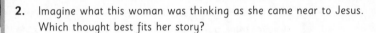 I'm sure Jesus will be happy to help me. It's easy for him.

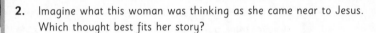 I'm nothing special. Someone like me can't just ask Jesus. But he is the powerful healer so I'll just touch his clothes.

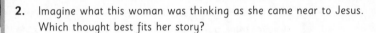 I can't imagine Jesus is different to all those doctors. I don't expect anything will happen, but I might as well try.

3. Look at what happened to the woman when she touched Jesus (v 29)
   How would you expect her to feel when she knew she was healed?

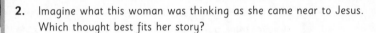 How did she feel when Jesus asked who had touched him (v 33)?

4. Jesus seemed to make her feel worse by calling her out of the crowd.
   Why do you think he did that?

**DOWNLOAD 3:1**

(Summary on p44)

5.  How do people treat Jesus today? Look at the following attitudes. Which are true of people you know?

■ "I never think about Jesus."

■ "He is too powerful and far away for us to really know. It's better to pray to saints."

■ "Jesus was someone special in history. He said some good things, but he's nothing to do with my life today."

■ "It's all right for women, children or old people to be interested in Jesus, but not for blokes."

■ "He's a source of power that I can plug into when I need help."

■ "I like the stories about Jesus and I want my children to know them."

6.  This story shows that Jesus has amazing power. So how should we treat him?

**Ask yourself:**

■ How do I treat Jesus?

# "Hurry Up, Jesus"

**Listen to the second part of the story: Mark 5 v 22-24 and 35-43**
You can read it yourself on p31-32.

1. Compare Jairus with the woman who has just been healed.

■ What is different?

■ What is similar?

2. In this story Jairus and the woman both need help. Think about how you would decide which person to help first. (These questions will help you answer this.)

■ How quickly did Jairus need help?

■ How quickly did the woman need help?

■ So who would you choose to help first?

**3.** How would you have felt if you were Jairus…

■ while Jesus was talking to the woman?

■ when the news of his daughter's death came?

**4.** How could it help Jairus to see the sick woman healed?

**5.** Think about how we respond to a death. Then look at what Jesus says in the following verses. In what way is Jesus different from us?

■ v 36:

■ v 39:

**6.** What did the people at Jairus' house think of Jesus?

■ Did they have a point?

**DOWNLOAD 3:2**

(Summary on p44)

**Ask yourself:**

▢ Am I trusting Jesus to change my death into life?

# Why bother with Jesus?

**Think about it**

**1.** What do the messengers say to Jairus (v 35)?

■ Does it sound like good advice?

■ Why is it bad advice?

**2.** Remember the questions at the beginning of this session?

▢ Has anyone ever found a cure for death?
▢ How can we comfort ourselves when death comes?

■ How could you now answer these questions differently?

30

3. Why should we **bother** Jesus (see verse 36)?

And why should we bother **with** him?

**Ask yourself:**

Death is coming to me. Have I "bothered" Jesus?

**DOWNLOAD 3:3**

(Summary on p44)

## The big questions

What truth about Jesus has this story shown you?

What need does this story make you face up to?

"The wages of sin is death, but the gift of God is eternal life in Christ Jesus our Lord."

Romans 6 v 23 (The Bible: New International Version)

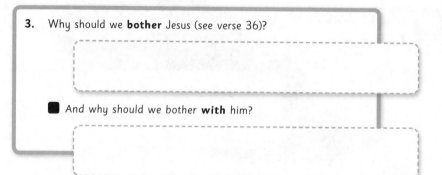

**My questions and comments**

# 3 Bible text

## The sick woman and the dying girl   Mark 5 v 21-43

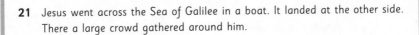

**21** Jesus went across the Sea of Galilee in a boat. It landed at the other side. There a large crowd gathered around him.

**22** Then a man named Jairus came. He was a synagogue ruler. Seeing Jesus, he fell at his feet.

**23** He begged Jesus, "Please come. My little daughter is dying. Place your hands on her to heal her. Then she will live."

**24** So Jesus went with him. A large group of people followed. They crowded around him.

**25** A woman was there who had a sickness that made her bleed. It had lasted for 12 years.

**26** She had suffered a great deal, even though she had gone to many doctors. She had spent all the money she had. But she was getting worse, not better.

**27** Then she heard about Jesus. She came up behind him in the crowd and touched his clothes.

**28** She thought, "I just need to touch his clothes. Then I will be healed."

**29** Right away her bleeding stopped. She felt in her body that her suffering was over.

**30** At once Jesus knew that power had gone out from him. He turned around in the crowd. He asked, "Who touched my clothes?"

**31** "You see the people," his disciples answered. "They are crowding against you. And you still ask, 'Who touched me?'"

**32** But Jesus kept looking around. He wanted to see who had touched him.

**33** Then the woman came and fell at his feet. She knew what had happened to her. She was shaking with fear. But she told him the whole truth.

**34** He said to her, "Dear woman, your faith has healed you. Go in peace. You are free from your suffering."

**35** While Jesus was still speaking, some people came from the house of Jairus. He was the synagogue ruler. "Your daughter is dead," they said. "Why bother the teacher anymore?"

**36** But Jesus didn't listen to them. He told the synagogue ruler, "Don't be afraid. Just believe."

**37** He let only Peter, James, and John, the brother of James, follow him.

**38** They came to the home of the synagogue ruler. There Jesus saw a lot of confusion. People were crying and sobbing loudly.

**39** He went inside. Then he said to them, "Why all this confusion and sobbing? The child is not dead. She is only sleeping."

**40** But they laughed at him. He made them all go outside. He took only the child's father and mother and the disciples who were with him. And he went in where the child was.

**41** He took her by the hand. Then he said to her, "Talitha koum!" This means, "Little girl, I say to you, get up!"

**42** The girl was 12 years old. Right away she stood up and walked around. They were totally amazed at this.

**43** Jesus gave strict orders not to let anyone know what had happened. And he told them to give her something to eat.

# 4 The blind beggar
## Mark 10 v 32-34 and 45-52

**Summary so far:**

- Jesus is the sin-forgiver because Jesus is God. Only he can help people like us, who are helpless, hopeless outcasts from God.
- Jesus is the "stronger man". Only he can rescue us from the power of Satan
- Jesus is the life-giver. He took the wages of sin that he didn't earn—death—to give those who trust in him what we cannot earn—life for ever.

### Think about what happens if someone like a king, queen or president visits your town...

- What things need to happen before the visit?

- What kinds of people are chosen to meet this very important person?

- What kinds of people are stopped from meeting them?

### The story

- Listen to this true story about Jesus: Mark 10 v 32-34 and 45-52
- You can read it for yourself on p40-41.

**Test yourself:** how much can you remember?
Answer the questions (in pairs, if you prefer).

Jesus and his disciples were on their way to the city of ¹_____. The
disciples were amazed that Jesus was going there, and some of Jesus' followers
felt ²_____. Jesus told them that the Son of ³_____ (that's
what he called himself) would be arrested by the Jewish leaders and sentenced to
⁴_____. But three days later he would ⁵_____.
Jesus also told his followers that he didn't come to be served, but to serve others. He
came to give ⁶_____ as the price for setting many people free.

On their journey they came to the city of ⁷_____. As they were leaving
the city, they passed a ⁸_____ man, sitting by the side of the road begging.
His name was Bartimaeus, which means ⁹"_____ of Timaeus". Bartimaeus
heard that Jesus of Nazareth was passing by. He began to shout: "Jesus, Son of
¹⁰_____! Have ¹¹_____ on me!" Many people told him to be
¹²_____. But he shouted even louder. Jesus wanted to meet him. So the
people told him that Jesus was calling for him. He threw his ¹³_____ to one
side, jumped to his feet and came to Jesus. "What ¹⁴_____
_____?" Jesus asked him. The blind man said: "Rabbi (Teacher), I want
to be able to see." Jesus told him: "Go. Your faith has healed you." Immediately he
could see and he ¹⁵_____ along the road.

# The Servant King

**Listen to the first part of the story again: Mark 10 v 32-34 and verse 45**
You can read it for yourself on p40.

### Think about it

**1.** What will happen in Jerusalem?

**2.** Jesus already knows this so why is he still going there? (Look at verse 45.)

**3.** Jesus calls himself the Son of Man, which means "God's chosen king". Look again at verse 45. What kind of king is he? How is he different from kings in this world?

**DOWNLOAD 4:1**

(Summary on p45)

**4.** Some people think of Jesus only as a helpless baby in a manger. He's lovable and makes you feel nice.

Others think of him as a powerful, distant figure in a stained-glass window. He's too busy and important to take any notice of you.

■ What's wrong with both of these views?

### Ask yourself:

■ Do I understand that Jesus is God's king?
■ Do I understand how Jesus came to serve others?
■ How should I respond to Jesus?

# Who's really blind?

**Listen to the second part of the story: Mark 10 v 46-50**
You can read it for yourself on p40-41.

### Think about it

1.  The beggar was blind, but what truth about Jesus could he see?

2.  Look at the blind beggar in verse 48. How did he show his faith in Jesus?

3.  The crowd tried to stop the beggar from meeting Jesus. But Jesus stopped to help the beggar. What does this tell us about...

■ the crowd's view of Jesus?

■ the truth about Jesus?

**DOWNLOAD 4:2**

(Summary on p45)

**4.** Many people call to Jesus/God for help. But not like this beggar.

■ The beggar didn't bargain with Jesus. He asked for mercy because he knew that Jesus is God's chosen king.
But how do people try to bargain with Jesus/God?

■ The beggar didn't give up when people told him to stop.
What things make us give up calling to Jesus/God for mercy?

■ The beggar understood that Jesus was the Servant King. But people often think of Jesus as only a servant or only a king.
How do people treat Jesus only as a servant?

■ How do people feel about Jesus when they hear only that he is king?

### Ask yourself:

■ Is there anyone trying to stop me from coming to Jesus?
■ What should I do about that?

# Saviour

**Listen to the last part of the story: Mark 10 v 51-52**
You can read it for yourself on p41.

1.  Look at Jesus' question in verse 51. What's strange about this question?

2.  At the end of the story...

■ what happens to the beggar?

■ where does he go?

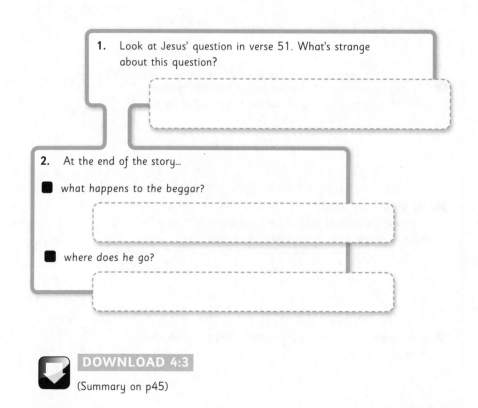

**DOWNLOAD 4:3**
(Summary on p45)

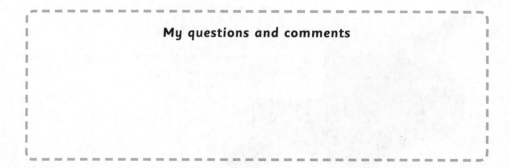

**My questions and comments**

## The big question: Where am I in the chart?

| Who did Jesus help? | What was their problem? | How does Jesus' death on the cross help? | What do we need to do? | Am I like this person... | |
|---|---|---|---|---|---|
| | | | | before they met Jesus? (✗ or ✓) | after they met Jesus? (✗ or ✓) |
| The paralysed man | A sinner. A helpless, hopeless outcast from God. | All sin can be forgiven. | Come to Jesus for forgiveness. | | |
| The man with the demon | Under the power of Satan. | Satan has been defeated. | Ask Jesus, the stronger man, to set you free. | | |
| The sick woman | Unclean. An outcast from God. | People made clean and right with God. | Come to Jesus for help and trust in him alone. | | |
| Jairus and his daughter | She was dead. | Death has been defeated. | Come to Jesus for help and trust in him alone. | | |
| The blind beggar | Blind and a helpless, hopeless outcast. | Jesus' followers can have new life. | Call to Jesus for mercy and follow him. | | |

"[Jesus] came to give his life as the price for setting many people free."
Mark 10 v 45 (The Bible: New International Reader's Version)

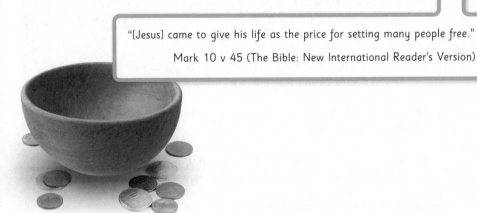

# 4 Bible text

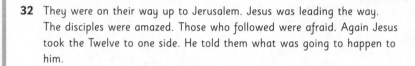

## The blind beggar
### Mark 10 v 32-34

**32** They were on their way up to Jerusalem. Jesus was leading the way. The disciples were amazed. Those who followed were afraid. Again Jesus took the Twelve to one side. He told them what was going to happen to him.

**33** "We are going up to Jerusalem," he said. "The Son of Man will be handed over to the chief priests and the teachers of the law. They will sentence him to death. Then they will hand him over to people who are not Jews.

**34** "The people will make fun of him and spit on him. They will whip him and kill him. Three days later he will rise from the dead!"

### Mark 10 v 45-52

**45** "Even the Son of Man did not come to be served. Instead, he came to serve others. He came to give his life as the price for setting many people free."

**46** Jesus and his disciples came to Jericho. They were leaving the city. A large crowd was with them. A blind man was sitting by the side of the road begging. His name was Bartimaeus. Bartimaeus means Son of Timaeus.

**47** He heard that Jesus of Nazareth was passing by. So he began to shout, "Jesus! Son of David! Have mercy on me!"

**48** Many people commanded him to stop. They told him to be quiet. But he shouted even louder, "Son of David! Have mercy on me!"

**49** Jesus stopped and said, "Call for him." So they called out to the blind man, "Cheer up! Get up on your feet! Jesus is calling for you."

**50** He threw his coat to one side. Then he jumped to his feet and came to Jesus.

**51** "What do you want me to do for you?" Jesus asked him. The blind man said, "Rabbi, I want to be able to see."

**52** "Go," said Jesus. "Your faith has healed you." Right away he could see. And he followed Jesus along the road.

# Downloads

Here is a summary of each Download to help you remember what was said.

## DOWNLOAD 1:1

- The paralysed man had a desperate need. He was a helpless, hopeless outcast.
- His friends believed that only Jesus could help him. You can see their faith in Jesus—they broke through the roof to reach Jesus.
- Instead of healing the paralysed man, Jesus told him: "Friend, your sins are forgiven".
- We think that the man's greatest need was to be healed. But Jesus saw that the man's greatest need was to have his sins forgiven.
- The word "sin" means "missing the mark" (like an arrow that misses the target).
- Sin is missing the mark of trusting and loving God. All of us fail to love God and his ways—good ways which he designed us to follow. So all of us are sinners. We all need to have our sins forgiven.

## DOWNLOAD 1:2

- The religious leaders were right to say that only God can forgive sins. That is because sin is "not loving God and his ways".
- They were also right to question whether Jesus was evil. That is because it is a terrible crime for humans to make themselves out to be God, or to take God's place.
- The big question is: who is Jesus? Is he lying or crazy when he says he can forgive sins? Or is he God, who truly can forgive sins?
- When we listen to what Jesus says, we have to decide who he is.
- We need to check out the evidence about who Jesus is.

## DOWNLOAD 1:3

- When Jesus healed this man, he was instantly no longer a helpless, hopeless outcast.
- When Jesus forgave this man's sins, he was instantly no longer a helpless, hopeless outcast from God.
- The man's healing is a picture of the difference that it makes when God forgives our sin.
- The friends' faith in Jesus meant that nothing could stop them coming to him.
- If we are to have our sins forgiven by Jesus, we must make sure that nothing stops us from coming to him.

## DOWNLOAD 2:1

- There is something worse in our world than just people making mistakes.
- The Bible tells us about a prince of evil called Satan or the devil or Beelzebub. His goal is to ruin and destroy everything that God has made.
- Amazingly, some people said Jesus was using the power of Beelzebub (or Satan) when he healed the man who couldn't speak.
- Beelzebub, "lord of the flies", brings death and decay. How could Jesus be using the power of death and decay when in fact he was healing the man?
- Jesus showed that these people were wrong. Jesus didn't work for Satan. Instead, he destroyed Satan's work.
- No one else could do what Jesus did. Jesus drove out demons with God's power.

## DOWNLOAD 2:2

- Jesus explains that Satan is like a strong man who has many weapons to keep his possessions safe.
- We are like the possessions of the strong man. Satan uses lies and deceit to keep all of us out of God's kingdom. We can't escape from Satan's influence and lies.
- Jesus tells us that we need a rescuer—a stronger man who can defeat Satan and his lies.
- Jesus is the stronger man. He defeated the powers of evil when he died on the cross. Because of what Jesus has done, we can be set free from Satan's kingdom and join God's kingdom.
- Jesus sacrificed himself so we can be rescued.
- We can't do anything to help ourselves by our own effort. We need Jesus to rescue us.

## DOWNLOAD 2:3

- Jesus tells a second story about people who try to live a better life instead of asking Jesus to rescue them.
- When someone realises they are living wrongly, they may decide to change, give up those wrong things and even start following a religion. They are like a house which has been swept clean and made neat.
- People who do this come to believe that God is pleased with them, because of the new way in which they now live.
- This is a big lie of Satan. God can never be pleased with us until our sin has been forgiven and Jesus is our king.
- People who think they are good enough for God don't come to Jesus for forgiveness and rescue. So they cannot be forgiven and rescued from Satan's power. They are like the clean house, where more evil spirits come to live at the end than in the beginning.
- The religious leaders thought they were good enough for God. Jesus was the rescuer they didn't want. That's why they tried to say that Jesus was evil.
- If you are not "with Jesus, then you are against him. It doesn't matter how good or religious you are. What matters is whether Jesus is your rescuer.

## DOWNLOAD 3:1

- The woman's medical problem was a hopeless case. Nothing could help her to get better.
- The woman's illness made her "unclean". The religious rules of that time said that she couldn't go to the temple to worship God. Anyone who touched her would become unclean too.
- When the woman touched Jesus' clothes, an exchange or swap took place. She received amazing health and cleanness, but Jesus became unclean.
- Jesus made the woman come and meet him. He wanted to know her, and he wanted her to know him.
- Jesus spoke lovingly to her. He was happy to become unclean so that she could become clean.
- Even though the woman knew she was unclean, that didn't stop her coming to Jesus. She had faith in him.

## DOWNLOAD 3:2

- Although Jairus' daughter was dying, Jesus stopped to speak to the sick woman, who wasn't dying at that moment.
- But Jesus didn't have to rush like an ambulance, for he has power over life and death.
- Jesus showed this power when he gave up his life and died on a cross, but rose to life again three days later.
- Jesus uses this power for his followers too. He promises that whoever believes in him will live even though they die.
- Jesus showed that he can keep this promise by raising the dead girl to life. He brought her back to life as easily as waking someone who is asleep.
- If we believe in Jesus, when we die Jesus will raise us to new life.

## DOWNLOAD 3:3

- So far, we've seen that we need a sin-forgiver, a rescuer from the power of Satan, and a life-giver because we are under the power of death.
- We are all going to die because we have earned the wages of sin. We are separated from God, the life-giver, because we don't love God and his ways.
- But the gift of God is eternal life in Jesus Christ— a free gift for us, but costly for Jesus.
- On the cross there was an exchange or swap. When Jesus died, he took the wages of sin, that he didn't earn. He did this to give us life, the gift that we couldn't earn.
- Like Jairus and the woman, we need to trust in Jesus and what he did on the cross.

## DOWNLOAD 4:1

- Jesus was on his way to Jerusalem, knowing that he was going to die a slow and terrible death there.
- Jesus called himself the Son of Man, which means "God's chosen king". He is the king of the universe.
- Jesus is also called the Son of David. This means that he is the one from the family of Israel's greatest king, David, who God has promised will be king for ever.
- As you would expect from the Son of Man, Jesus not only knew what would happen in Jerusalem; he planned that it would happen.
- In Mark 10 v 45 Jesus tells us what kind of king he is—a Servant King.

## DOWNLOAD 4:2

- Jesus, the king of the universe, is on his way to Jerusalem, where he will be killed. But in Jericho people welcome him like a king.
- A blind beggar understands that Jesus is God's chosen king, and calls out to him for mercy.
- The crowd tell the beggar to be silent. They are treating Jesus like a king but they don't understand that he is the Servant King.
- Although the beggar is blind, only he can see that he desperately needs mercy. He also sees that only Jesus the king can give him mercy.
- Jesus responds to the beggar's call by calling him.

## DOWNLOAD 4:3

- Jesus asks the beggar: "What do you want me to do for you?"
- It's an important question because the beggar's whole life must change if Jesus heals him. And the change might not be comfortable.
- The beggar wants this new life. When Jesus heals him, he follows Jesus along the road. He is following Jesus to Jerusalem, where Jesus will die.
- Jesus tells the beggar that his faith in Jesus has healed (or "saved") him.
- Jesus the Servant King died on the cross to save us from our sins, the power of Satan and the power of death. Faith (trust) in Jesus saves us from all these enemies.
- Jesus is calling us to follow him. Will you put your trust in him and do that?

**Notes and comments:**

**Notes and comments:**

**Notes and comments:**